This book belongs to

....

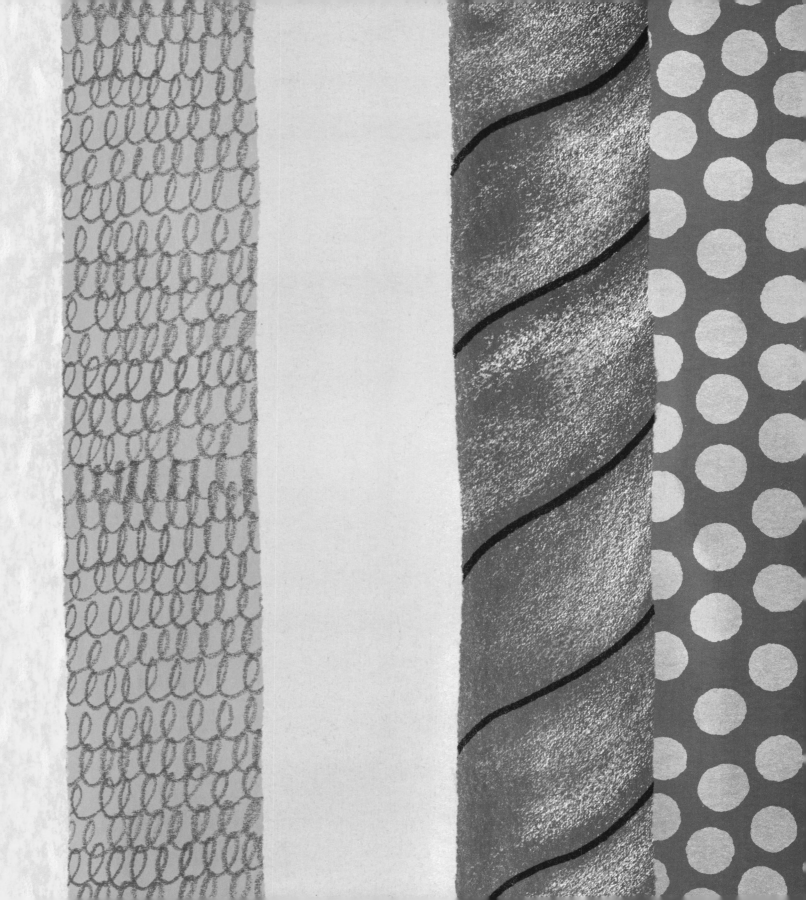

First published 2023 by Macmillan Children's Books
an imprint of Pan Macmillan
The Smithson, 6 Briset Street, London EC1M 5NR
EU representative: Macmillan Publishers Ireland Limited,
1st Floor, The Liffey Trust Centre, 117–126 Sheriff Street Upper, Dublin 1, D01 YC43
Associated companies throughout the world

www.panmacmillan.com

ISBN: 978-1-5290-9294-3

Printed in China

MIX
Paper | Supporting
responsible forestry
FSC
www.fsc.org
FSC® C116313

This Little UNICORN

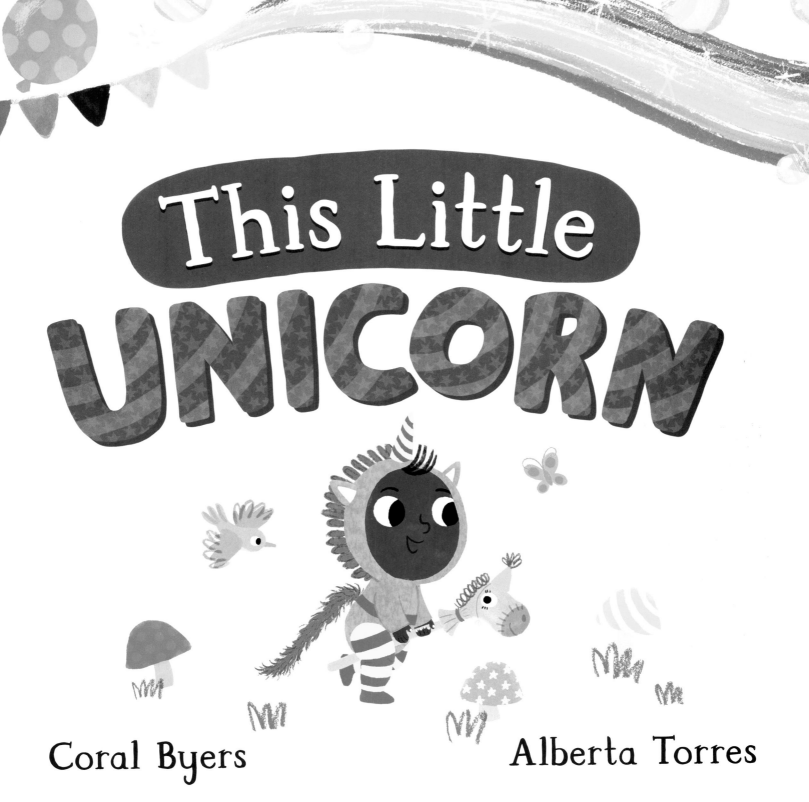

Coral Byers

Alberta Torres

Macmillan Children's Books

This little unicorn
dances and prances

1

This little unicorn
swishes and **swirls**

2

This little unicorn
frolics and flitters

And this little unicorn
twists and **twirls!**

4

This little unicorn
chomps and crunches

This little unicorn's having a snooze!

This little
unicorn pulls
the ribbon . . .

Which treats would **YOU** choose?

7

This little unicorn
flaps and flutters

8

This little unicorn wants to try!

9

This little unicorn flies up, up, up . . .

And gallops across a rainbow sky!

10

And all the little unicorns go . . .

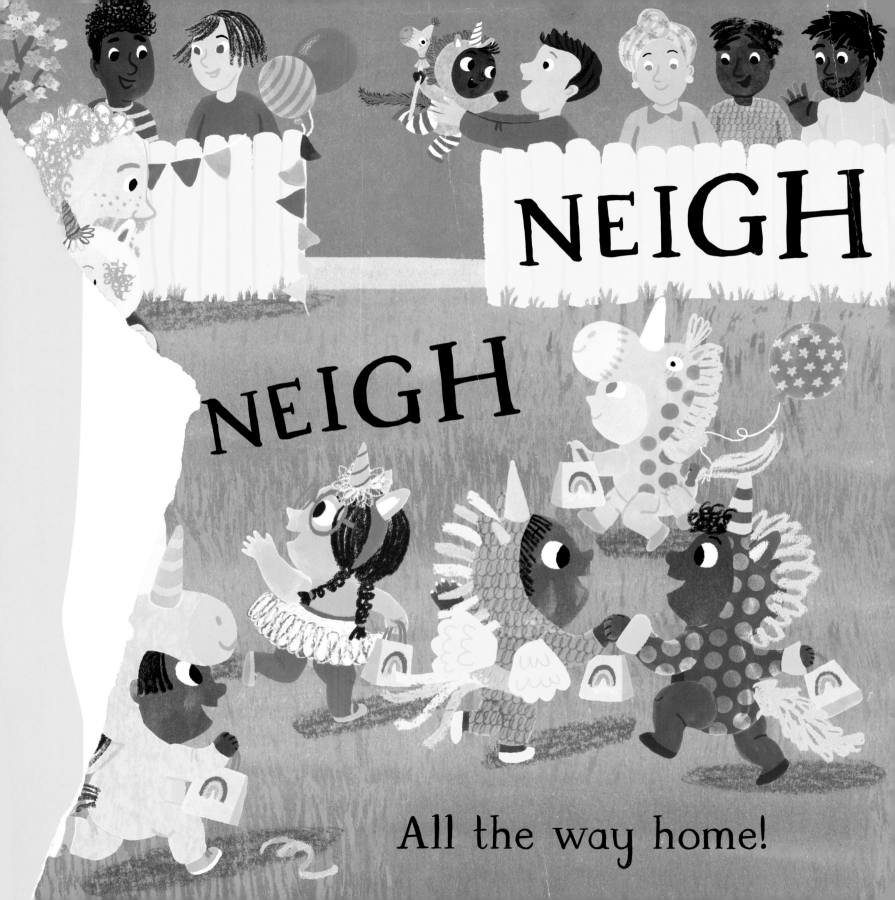

NEIGH

NEIGH

All the way home!

Reading Together
Tips for Parents and Carers

This book has been specially created and developed for preschool children. It uses the popular nursery rhyme *This Little Piggy* to create an instantly familiar, read-aloud preschool adventure!

- The fun, repetitive and rhythmic text helps develop language and vocabulary.

- The bar along the bottom counts from 1 to 10, with numbers on each page to help children recognise numerals.

- There is a page at the back of the book with more information about the children, to give extra talking points about different personalities, likes and dislikes, and opinions.

- There is plenty of evidence to show that sharing books and reading together helps children to communicate, develop ideas and understanding, and gives them a head start at school. But the most important thing is to enjoy the closeness of sharing a book together.

When you read this book together, you could talk to your child about...

... the ten children in the book. Can your child find and count each one as you go along? **What is each child doing?** You could encourage your child to join in and mimic the children's actions.

... how the children's world changes into **an imaginative make-believe world** as they play. What can your child see change as they turn the pages?

... things around you that your child could use to **create their own make-believe world.** What would they like to dress up as? What kind of birthday party would they like to have?

... the numbers in the book — can they find and **read each number?** Try reading the book while your child counts each little unicorn on their fingers or toes, just like in the nursery rhyme.

Say Hello to the Unicorns!

1 **Aisha** wants to eat birthday cake every day!

2 **Felix** is learning to ride a bike.

3 **Grace**'s favourite animal is a rabbit.

4 **Ezra** loves to draw colourful rainbows.

5 **Benjamin**'s mummy is going to have a baby soon!

6 **Muhammed**'s favourite colour is yellow.

7 **Evie**'s middle name is Alice.

8 **Noa** is going on holiday on an aeroplane!

9 **Max** can write his own name!

10 **Iris** likes to sing songs and dance around.

What will they all dress up as next?